Contents

 Fiction

The Basilisk's Head
page 2

 **Non-fiction**

Roman Slaves
page 14

Written by
Alison Hawes

Illustrated by
Ollie Cuthbertson

Series editor **Dee Reid**

TRELOAR COLLEGE Sd
R26928P2386

Heinemann
Part of Pearson

The Basilisk's Head — page 2
Roman Slaves — page 14

Characters

Salan

The King

The Basilisk

Tricky words

- closer
- coming
- cloak
- shield
- shines
- mirror

Read these words to the student. Help them with these words when they appear in the text.

Introduction

Salan is a slave. He wants to be free. But the evil King will only grant Salan his freedom if he can do four difficult and dangerous tasks.

One of Salan's tasks is to kill the basilisk and take the basilisk's head back to the King.

THE BASILISK'S HEAD

Salan must look for the basilisk,
if he wants to be free.
But he must look out!
For just one look from the basilisk
will turn him to stone!

Salan comes to the basilisk's cave.
He sees some people outside the cave.
But as Salan gets closer to the cave,
he sees that all the people are
made of stone!

Then the basilisk comes out of the cave.
It looks for Salan.
Salan hears the basilisk coming closer.
I must not look at it, he thinks.

The basilisk goes back into the cave.
Salan looks in his bag.
He sees his cloak and his shield.
He has a plan to get the basilisk's head.
Salan rubs his shield with his cloak.
He rubs and rubs.
Soon his shield shines like a mirror.

Then he calls out to the basilisk.
"Come and get me," Salan calls.
I must not look at it, he thinks.
*One look from the basilisk will
turn me to stone.*

The basilisk comes out of the cave.
It looks at Salan's shield.
It is like looking into a mirror.

The basilisk turns to stone!

The head snaps off the stone basilisk.

Salan puts the basilisk's head in his bag.
"I will take it to the King," he says.
"Then soon, I will be free!"

Quiz

Text comprehension

Literal comprehension

p6 Why does Salan rub his shield with his cloak?

p9 How does Salan defeat the basilisk?

Inferential comprehension

p4 Who are the people made of stone?

p5 How do you think the basilisk knew Salan was near his cave?

p8 Why did Salan call out to the basilisk?

Personal response

- Do you think Salan is clever? Why?
- Think of another way to kill a basilisk.

Word knowledge

p4 Find a word meaning the opposite of 'inside'.

p6 Find a simile. What two things are being compared?

p11 Find a powerful verb.

Spelling challenge

Read these words:

come   her   from

Now try to spell them!

Ha! Ha! Ha!

What is a snake's favourite subject?

Hisstory!

Find out about

- the hard life of a slave in Roman times.

Tricky words

- slaves
- bought
- prisoners
- forced
- gladiators
- beaten
- Spartacus
- thousands

Read these words to the student. Help them with these words when they appear in the text.

Introduction

The Romans had lots of slaves who had to work for no pay.
They bought and sold slaves in the slave market.
Many slaves were prisoners of war. Some slaves were forced
to fight as gladiators or in the Roman army. Spartacus was a
slave who ran away but he was caught and killed.

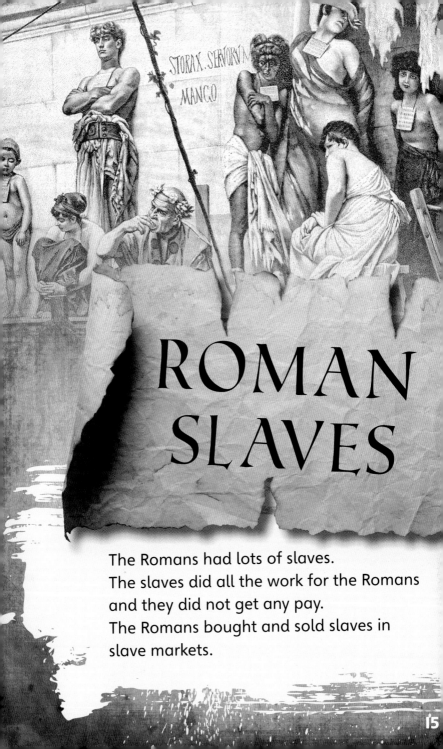

ROMAN SLAVES

The Romans had lots of slaves.
The slaves did all the work for the Romans
and they did not get any pay.
The Romans bought and sold slaves in
slave markets.

Most of the slaves the Romans bought and sold were prisoners of war.

Sometimes poor Romans
sold their children as slaves.

Some slaves were forced to fight as gladiators.
Some slaves were forced to fight in the Roman army.

Some slaves were forced to work on the Roman war ships.

Some slaves were made to work in Roman homes or on farms.

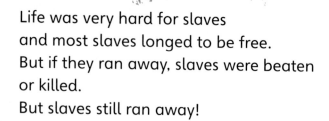

Life was very hard for slaves
and most slaves longed to be free.
But if they ran away, slaves were beaten
or killed.
But slaves still ran away!

Spartacus was a slave who was forced
to fight as a gladiator.
He longed to be free, so he and
80 other gladiators ran away.

Thousands of other slaves ran away
to be in his slave army.
But in the end, his army was beaten
and he was killed by the Roman army.

Some slaves were lucky.
If they were good as gladiators
they might win their freedom.
If they were good in the army
they might win their freedom.
But most slaves lived and died as slaves.

Text comprehension

Literal comprehension
p20 What happened to slaves who tried to run away?
p23 How did some slaves win their freedom?

Inferential comprehension
p17 Why do you think some Romans sold their children as slaves?
p20 Do you think the Romans treated their slaves fairly?
p20 Why do you think slaves risked running away?

Personal response
• If you were a slave, what work would you prefer to do?
• Would you have joined Spartacus' army?

Word knowledge

p18 How many syllables are there in the word 'gladiators'?
p20 Find a word meaning 'wished'.
p20 Find seven words in the word 'beaten'.

Spelling challenge

Read these words:

one   very   want

Now try to spell them!

Ha! Ha! Ha!

Where does the General keep his armies?

Up his sleevies!